Adopting a Little Brother or Sister

Written by Holly Marlow

Illustrated by Zoe Marlow

ISBN 978-1-7399168-1-7

DEDICATION

For my amazing children, who inspired me to create this book. I love you both incredibly much, and I always will.

ACKNOWLEDGEMENTS

Endless thanks to my wonderful husband Jon, who has supported me in so many ways. Love you always.

Special thanks to my imaginative superstar, Zoe, for creating the beautiful artwork that makes this book fun!

So you're adopting a little brother or sister, huh?
WOOHOO! That's so exciting!

It's GREAT being the big sibling! My family adopted a baby brother and we have so much fun together!

It takes aaaages to adopt a child. Have you been waiting for long? Don't worry, it's totally worth it!

I was a bit frustrated at first, because some of my friends had baby brothers and sisters already, but they were tiny babies, who couldn't play for months.

When we adopted my little brother, he was already old enough to play! That was so cool.

We had lots of visits from social workers. They were friendly people, who asked my parents HUNDREDS of questions. One of them wore really cool socks!

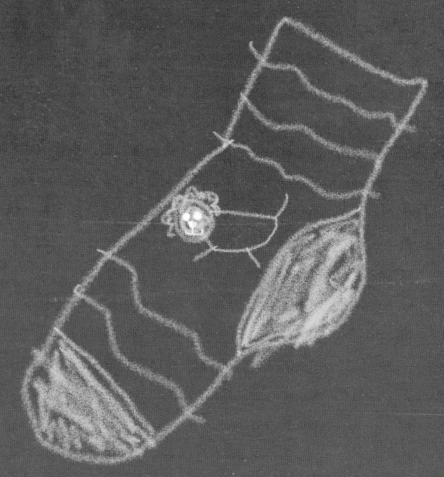

The social workers have to learn all about you and your family, so that they can make sure they find the exact right child for your family, and the exact right family for each child.

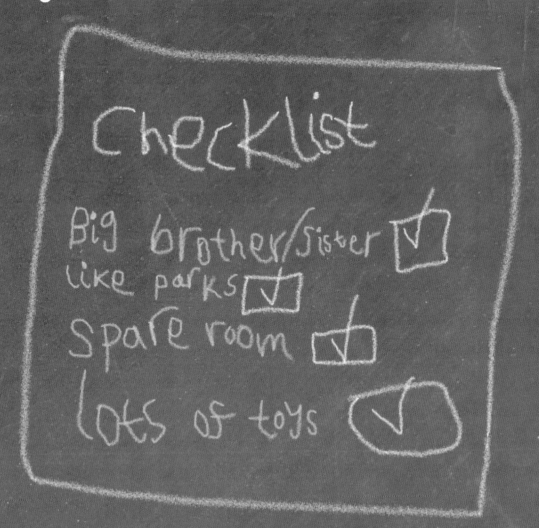

One of the social workers asked me what I thought it would be like to be a big sister. I said I wanted to adopt LOTS of brothers and sisters!

She said perhaps we should just start with one and see how that goes.

We talked about what it would be like to have to share my toys. I told her I'm really good at sharing already, because I share with my friends.

So like I said, it takes aaaaaaaaaaages, but there was a lot to do while we waited for the social workers to find the right baby. I helped my parents to get the baby's room ready.

We got out all the old baby toys from when I was little, and I was in charge of checking they still worked. We got a few new toys too, so I checked them as well!

FINALLY, my parents told me that the social workers had found a little boy who needed a family just like ours, with a big sister! I was so excited! They showed me a photo of him. He looked happy and cheeky!

We couldn't just go and collect him straight away. It's not like shopping, you know. You can't just go and pick up a brother or sister. I kind of wished you could. That would have been faster!

My little brother was living with a foster family.
Do you know what that is?

Foster families are families who love children and look after them until the social workers find the exact right family for them to live with forever.

My brother didn't know us yet and thought the foster family were his family. Well, they kind of were his family, just for a while. He was too little to understand, so we had to help him learn that we're his new family.

I chose a special teddy for him and recorded a message, saying "I'm your big sister!" so that he would get used to my voice.

My parents made a book of photos of us and gave it to my brother's foster family. The foster parents showed him the photos and said "that's your big sister!" and "that's Mummy and Daddy!"

We spent a couple of weeks getting to know my little brother. First we had some video calls with him. Then we went to the foster family's house to play with him for a bit longer each day.

After a few days of playing, he knew us well enough that he wasn't nervous any more. We took him out for a walk in his buggy and the next day, he came and played at our house for a while.

That's me on the buggy board!

A few days later, my baby brother came to live with us forever. The social worker kept visiting us for a few months, to check that he was settling in well and that we were all getting used to him being in our family.

Now he's part of our family forever and we have lots of fun playing and having adventures together.

Suggested Discussion Questions

1. How old do you think your little brother or sister will be when we meet them? What do you think children that age like to do? What kind of toys do you think they will like to play with?

2. What kind of toys will not be safe for your new sibling to play with? Where should we put those toys? When do you think we will be able to play with those toys? (Perhaps naptime?)

3. How do you feel about sharing and taking turns? Are there some toys that will be harder to share than others? What shall we do if you don't feel like sharing a toy that's special to you?

4. What do you think social workers think about when they are matching a child to a family? (Some children need to be an only child, especially if they need a lot of attention, but others would really like to have a big brother or sister, especially if they had siblings in the foster family. Some are scared of or allergic to pets, but others would love to have pets in their family...)

5. How do you think your brother or sister will feel when they first meet us? Do you think they will know that we are safe, kind people? What do you think we should do to help them to settle in and feel at home with us?

About The Author

Holly Marlow is a British author and parent to both biological and adopted children. Holly strives for a gentle/therapeutic parenting style and this has led her to create stories to help children to understand some of the emotional and practical complexities of adoption.

Holly enjoys travelling (especially searching for chameleons, geckos and snakes in the wild parts of Africa) and learning foreign languages. Holly has fibromyalgia and has spent a lot of time trying to raise awareness of the chronic pain condition, giving presentations in schools and universities. Holly also enjoys baking and gardening, and is terrible at both.

This story is illustrated by Holly's talented daughter, Zoe, who at age 5 enjoys soft play, parks and creating her own illustrated stories and plays. Zoe was eager to provide the illustrations for this book. She created them in less than 10 minutes and has been wondering for months why it took her mother so long to finish the book.

Also by Holly Marlow

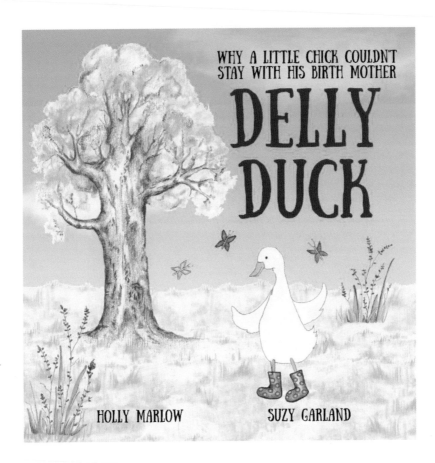

When Delly Duck lays an egg, she is excited for it to hatch. But she doesn't really know how to keep an egg safe, or how to look after her chick when he hatches. See how a concerned goose tries to help Delly to learn how to care for her chick, in this touching adoption story.

Delly Duck: Why a Little Chick Couldn't Stay with his Birth Mother is available in multiple languages.

Printed in Great Britain
by Amazon